CLIMBING HIGH

Mike Anderiesz

B❊XTREE

First published 2002 by Boxtree
an imprint of Pan Macmillan Ltd
Pan Macmillan, 20 New Wharf Road, London N1 9RR
Basingstoke and Oxford
Associated companies throughout the world
www.panmacmillan.com

ISBN 0 7522 1518 3

Rainbow is a trademark of Thames Television Ltd (a FremantleMedia company)
Copyright © 2002 FremantleMedia Enterprises Ltd.
Based on the Thames TV programme Rainbow
Licensed by Fremantle Brand Licensing
www.fremantlemedia.com/licensing

FREMANTLEMEDIA

Picture credits: all **Rainbow** photos copyright **FremantleMedia Enterprises Ltd**; **Rex Features London** pp 15, 15, 21, 28, 29, 30, 30, 31, 32, 33, 33, 36, 37, 38, 38, 38, 39, 51, 52, 53, 54, 54, 55, 58, 59, 65, 68, 68, 68, 68, 69, 71, 72, 74, 74, 75, 79, 80, 81, 87, 88, 91, 102, 102, 103, 103; **Popperfoto** p 14; **Popperfoto/Reuters** pp 43, 75; **The Academy of Motion Picture Arts and Sciences** p15.

The right of Mike Anderiesz to be identified as the
author of this work has been asserted by him in accordance
with the Copyright, Designs and Patents Act 1988.

9 8 7 6 5 4 3 2 1

A CIP catalogue record for this book is
available from the British Library.

Designed by seagulls
Printed by Butler and Tanner, Frome and London

Introduction

Hello. This is my book. I know you'll like it!

It's all about me, but there are bits about Geoffrey, George, Rod, Jane and Freddy and of course that great hairy bear Bungle! Ha ha. It's really about me though, and about how famous and popular I am.

Did you see my Marmite commercial this year? Good, wasn't it! This big advertising company came along and asked if I'd promote Marmite. They said, 'Will you be in our commercial?' I said, 'No way, I hate the stuff!' They said, 'Fantastic darling, just what we want.' So I said I'd do it and got them to pay me two jars of Marmite instead of one.

George said, 'But you don't even like Marmite, Zippy.' And I said, 'No, I hate it, but business is business, so shut up George and put that tiara back in the dressing-up box.' That's me, really clever and quick too!

As I said, I am very famous and popular. I get asked to do all sorts of things. Do you know they even talked about me being King. Yes. And people went round with boards which had 'Zippy for King' written on them. I had to stop them though, 'cos it was making George upset – he thinks Elvis is the only King.

If I can't be King I could always be Mayor or even Prime Minister. I'm thinking of starting a new party called the Rainbow Democrats. We stand for compulsory picnics in public places, sticky-back plastic to be available on the NHS, and zips to be fitted to all television presenters – especially Anne Robinson. Sensible policies for a sensible Britain. You'd join, wouldn't you?

Anyway, my book has fun and games from all the gang, a history of the show and, of course, I've got my very own chapters. I tell you all about the naughty secrets of children's television. I know they're naughty, 'cos I made them up!

Have fun with the book … I did!

1: Our Favourite Adventure (part 1)

It was a lovely sunny morning in late August and the gang were busy discussing how to spend their day.

'Let's all go to the Notting Hill Carnival!' said Zippy. 'I've got some banging dub grooves on a Ragga-tip that I want to try out ... Respect!'

'No, let's have a picnic …' said Bungle. 'I've made Marmite sandwiches and baked a cake – I even shampooed my fur with "Wash & Growl". Oh, yes, let's do that.'

'Carnival!' shouted Zippy
'Picnic!' replied Bungle
'Now hang on, you two …' said Geoffrey.
'What does George want to do?'

'Well, I think we should stay at home and try on funny costumes,' he said, doing just that.

'But that's what we've been doing every day since 1972!' snapped Zippy.
'Yes, and you were doing it even before that,' added Bungle.
'Oh, come on George,' said Geoffrey. 'Why not try something new
for a change? It's such a lovely day ...'

'I know, let's all go
for a drive in my taxi,
and we'll cruise around
town picking up birds.'

'What's that like, then?' asked Bungle. 'We've never tried picking up birds before.'
'Yes, is it dangerous?' added Zippy

'Not at all', said Geoffrey. 'I was the king of picking up birds when I was younger. It was easy, all you needed was a fast car, a lot of money and your own TV series. Anyone can do it!'

'Er … Geoffrey – is this the right idea?' asked George. 'Look, I've picked up a duck!'

'Yes, and I've picked up a goose ...'

'And look ... I've got a cock!' said
Geoffrey, getting rather carried away

'Actually ...' added
Bungle, from over in
corner, 'George migh
on to something with
dressing up idea – do
my bum look big in t

'Whatever ... let's just go, 'cos we've been arguing about this for nearly six hours and it's getting dark, and you know what happens after dark, don't you?'
'No?' they all exclaimed together
'Well, I could explain ...' said Geoffrey.
'But I'll bet Rod, Jane and Freddy know a song about it ...'

'When the moon is full and the night is dark,
Magical things start to play their part.
When the witches sing and the air gets nippy
You'd better watch out for ...'

' ... Evil Zippy!!!'

Oh no! What will happen when Evil Zippy gets back to the house and will it involve any more glaring continuity errors? Find out on page 104.

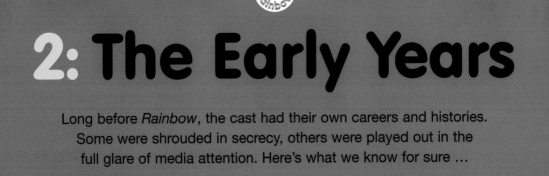

2: The Early Years

Long before *Rainbow*, the cast had their own careers and histories. Some were shrouded in secrecy, others were played out in the full glare of media attention. Here's what we know for sure ...

Bungle

Bungle was raised in darkest Peru where he used to stalk the tropical rainforests, foraging for food and scaring the natives. Although hidden for many years, we know he ventured beyond the woods thanks to regular sightings of 'a scary bear-like creature' thought to be Bigfoot or possibly Fergie. It was not until 1965, however, that he left the jungles to seek his fortune in the wider world.

Unfortunately, his first venture into public life turned into a media circus when he was involved in a bitter paternity suit with one Vanessa Del Puerto, a Brazilian actress and part-time model who accused him of abandoning his only child

several years earlier. Subsequent DNA tests proved him to be the father of an orphan bear-cub, later found abandoned at a railway station in England smuggling large quantities of marmalade in a small suitcase. The court demanded a six-figure alimony settlement and Bungle was forced to leave South America to seek work.

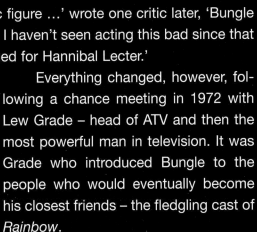

After several years working in Turkey as a dancing bear, his big break came in 1967 when he was cast opposite Charlton Heston in the cult classic, *Planet of the Apes*. Unfortunately, his scenes were left on the cutting room floor after unwelcome audience reactions to the test screenings.

' … Although Heston cuts a suitably heroic figure …' wrote one critic later, 'Bungle fares less well as the plucky chimp Cornelius. I haven't seen acting this bad since that yellow bear with a honey-pot fixation auditioned for Hannibal Lecter.'

Everything changed, however, following a chance meeting in 1972 with Lew Grade – head of ATV and then the most powerful man in television. It was Grade who introduced Bungle to the people who would eventually become his closest friends – the fledgling cast of *Rainbow*.

'Oh goody!' he said, 'I've finally found my calling …'

'Oh Christ' they replied 'There goes our chance of a BAFTA …'

Zippy

Of the entire *Rainbow* cast, Zippy's past is clouded in the greatest mystery. What exactly is he; why does he only have one hand; who in their right mind would fit a zip to a sentient life-form – these are all questions *Rainbow* enthusiasts have been debating for years. Zippy describes himself as 'unique', but beyond that the little we do know about him leads to even deeper questions.

Shortly after the Roswell incident, secret files from Area 51 mention the appearance of a saucer-shaped object entering Earth's atmosphere in 1951. According to the airforce pilot who saw it …

'It seems to be flying erratically, Sir, and laying a trail of black sticky liquid, possibly beef extract …'

The UFO later crashed in the Nevada desert and 'a Zippy-like creature' was seen in Las Vegas, gambling heavily on slot-

machines. After this, sporadic sightings across America linked him to various underworld activities. Indeed, an FBI report from 1967 went so far as to name him as Johnny 'the zip' Montana – a hitman for the powerful Velcrosi crime syndicate, reputed to taunt rival mobsters with the chilling line 'The next zip you see will be on a bodybag, amigo!'

After 1969, however, he disappeared from view entirely, resurfacing only when the original cast of *Rainbow* came together in 1972. Was this the same ruthless alien hoodlum or a totally different and undoubtedly gifted children's entertainer?

The truth is out there …

Well, it better be, 'cos it certainly ain't in here.

George

George was born in 1930, the only child of Gerry and Georgina Hippo of 23a, The Swamp, Nairobi. As a child he appeared in several Tarzan movies, on one occasion wrestling with Johnny Weissmuller until a court order prevented it happening again. Even at an early age, however, his parents were confused by his theatrical tendencies and odd mannerisms.

'Listen …' said his father. 'We get up in the mornings, we lie up to our ears in mud and occasionally roar – that's what we do, we're hippos!'

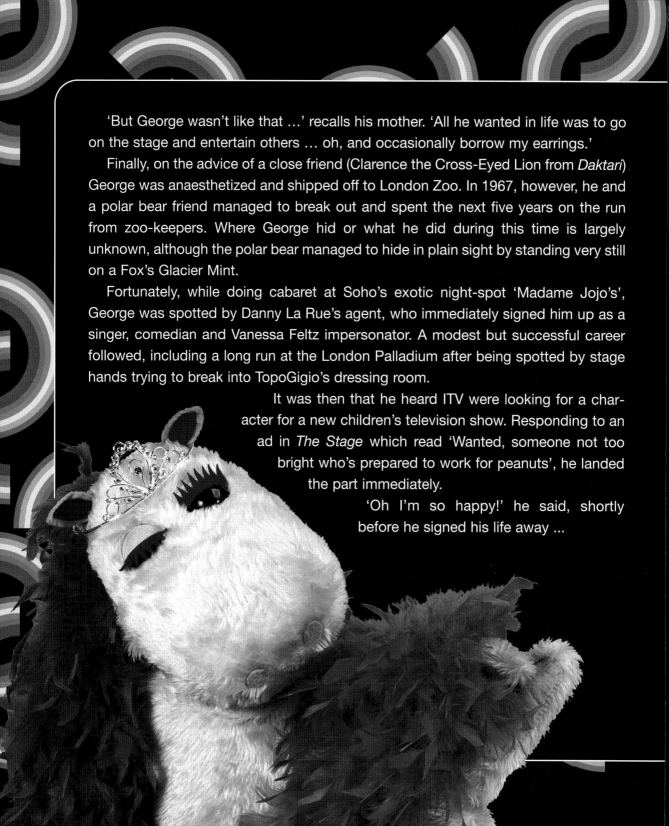

'But George wasn't like that ...' recalls his mother. 'All he wanted in life was to go on the stage and entertain others ... oh, and occasionally borrow my earrings.'

Finally, on the advice of a close friend (Clarence the Cross-Eyed Lion from *Daktari*) George was anaesthetized and shipped off to London Zoo. In 1967, however, he and a polar bear friend managed to break out and spent the next five years on the run from zoo-keepers. Where George hid or what he did during this time is largely unknown, although the polar bear managed to hide in plain sight by standing very still on a Fox's Glacier Mint.

Fortunately, while doing cabaret at Soho's exotic night-spot 'Madame Jojo's', George was spotted by Danny La Rue's agent, who immediately signed him up as a singer, comedian and Vanessa Feltz impersonator. A modest but successful career followed, including a long run at the London Palladium after being spotted by stage hands trying to break into TopoGigio's dressing room.

It was then that he heard ITV were looking for a character for a new children's television show. Responding to an ad in *The Stage* which read 'Wanted, someone not too bright who's prepared to work for peanuts', he landed the part immediately.

'Oh I'm so happy!' he said, shortly before he signed his life away ...

Geoffrey

When the full history of stage and screen is written, few names will rank higher than that of Geoffrey. One of the founders of 'method' acting, Marlon Brando once described him as 'possibly the true architect of modern cinema … but then again, possibly not.'

In his heyday as a performer, Geoffrey used to go to legendary lengths to become the characters he played, no matter how minor they appeared on the page. During a 1970 episode of *Softly, Softly*, for instance, his character was a petty felon with only one line ('You'll never take me, Rozzer!'). Nevertheless, to research the part correctly, Geoffrey knocked over a liquor store and spent six years in Wormwood Scrubs. Upon delivering his line, the cast stopped and applauded –

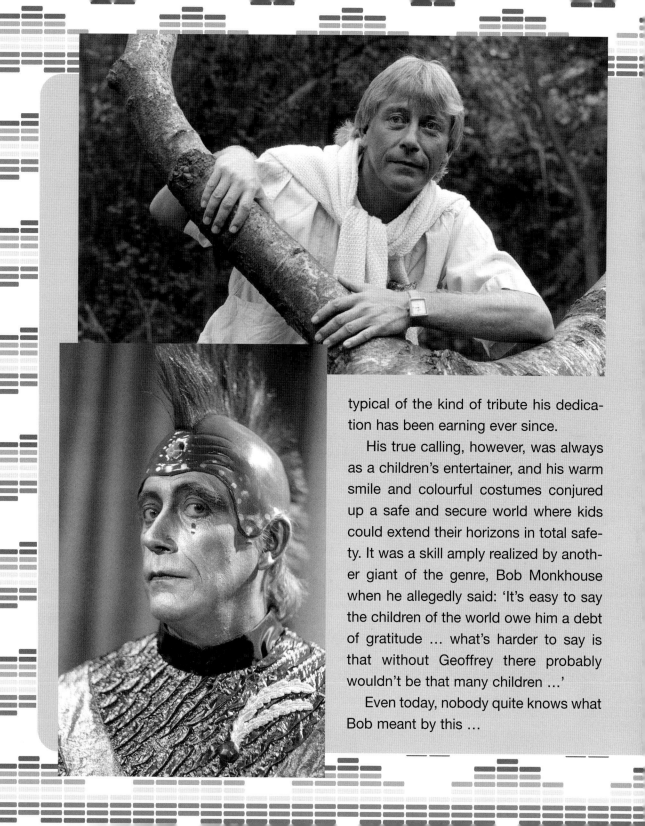

typical of the kind of tribute his dedication has been earning ever since.

His true calling, however, was always as a children's entertainer, and his warm smile and colourful costumes conjured up a safe and secure world where kids could extend their horizons in total safety. It was a skill amply realized by another giant of the genre, Bob Monkhouse when he allegedly said: 'It's easy to say the children of the world owe him a debt of gratitude … what's harder to say is that without Geoffrey there probably wouldn't be that many children …'

Even today, nobody quite knows what Bob meant by this …

3: George's Twenty Things U Never Knew About Rainbow

1 It was originally titled 'The world's most dangerous gangs'.

2 If you play the theme song backwards you can clearly hear the words 'Andy Pandy is the Antichrist'.

3 Geoffrey has an evil twin brother who is currently President of Swaziland.

4 Zippy claims to have taught Jamie Oliver everything he knows. 'Yes, and it took me less than five minutes,' he says. 'Six, if you count teaching him the difference between fresh herbs and nettles ...'

5 In the mid-1980s, I briefly dated Andrew Lloyd-Webber. It was an innocent mistake – I thought he was a hippo.

6 In 2001 Bungle became the first-ever space tourist sent by the Russians to the MIR space station. 'Ooh, what happens if I press this button?' he said, shortly before it crashed into the Pacific.

7 There is an organization called Rainbowholics Anonymous which meets once a month to offer support to those addicted to the programme. Members are encouraged to repeat the mantra 'I am not Geoffrey' and stay well away from bright colours.

8 In 1976 the producers tried to sue George Lucas, claiming uncanny similarities between one of his films and a *Rainbow* episode entitled 'Star Paws'.

9 Zippy has never been seen in the same place as Neil Kinnock. Draw your own conclusions.

10 US President George W Bush is so scared of Bungle he has the CIA keeping tracks on his movements.

11 Rod, Jane and Freddy have a long-standing rivalry with Mary, Mungo and Midge. 'One of these days they're going to get what's coming to them,' they allegedly said, shortly before the lift accident which saw all three BBC stars hospitalized.

Ritchie Blackmore's Rainbow was a heavy metal band and had nothing to do with **12** the show. Which is a pity because he was even hairier than Bungle and would have fitted right in.

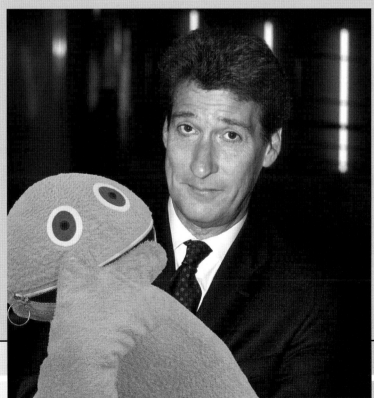

In 1995 Jeremy Paxman broke down in tears on *Newsnight* while **13** interviewing Zippy. 'He was just too quick for me,' he said later.

14 We are all national heroes in Australia, where the show was widely mistaken for a documentary about inner city life in Britain.

15 The show is so popular in China they have a 'National Rainbow Day', during which dissidents are rounded up and forced to do the same thing for up to twenty years.

16 'Randy, Fonder, Jaded' is an anagram of 'Rod, Jane and Freddy'.

17 Attempts to bring back the show last year failed when BBC2 pointed out they already had a thirty-minute programme showing adults behaving like little kids. Apparently it's called *Prime Minister's Questions*.

18 Bungle has never been seen in the same place as agony aunt Claire Rayner. Need I say more?

I have never been seen in the same place as Elton John. However, we do go to the same hairdresser.

19

20 During a 1989 palimony case between Mickey and Minnie Mouse, Geoffrey was cited as the cause of their break-up. 'She came round wanting to borrow some cheese,' he later admitted 'How was I supposed to know she was engaged?'

4: Dear Bungle

Hello everybody! Uncle Bungle here.

Not all of us went on to be megastars like Geoffrey and Zippy. In fact, I never cared much about fame or money – I liked helping people and making tea. This is why I became an 'agony bear' for a tabloid newspaper, a job which I have been doing for several years now.

I love writing my column and helping out readers wherever I can. In fact, shall we have a look at some of those letters now? Oh yes, let's do that, and we can laugh at the silly situations people get themselves into.

OK, here goes.

'Dear Uncle Bungle – I recently came home unexpectedly to find my girlfriend in bed with another woman and they were kissing. Now I feel so insecure. What shall I do?
– Worried, Carlisle'.

'Dear Worried – Girls are very different from us boys (or bears, for that matter). They like to get together and play with their dolls and make tea and hug and kiss, and some- times they do this in bed because it's all warm and cosy and Zippy isn't allowed in there. This is all quite natural. In fact, if you ask nicely, they may let you join in. Think what fun you could have then!'

You know what I like best? The letters that ask important questions about making the world a better place. Here's one:

'Dear Uncle Bungle – The ozone layer is depleting at a frightening rate
and we're all in danger of frying. Can you think of a solution that will still allow

the Americans to sell their oil and cigarettes, because I'm fresh out of ideas – *Yours, Kofi Annan'*.

'Dear Kofi (that's a funny name, isn't it children?) – It's very important that we all do our bit for recycling. For example, Geoffrey's taxi runs on diesel and Zippy recycles all his Marmite jars. As for me, I like to reuse answers to previous letters. So in conclusion, keep applying the cream and don't use that thing until the swelling goes down!'

However, even I can't always help my readers out, which makes me very sad. For example, I got this letter recently from someone who didn't even sign his name.

'Dear Uncle Bungle – People often say to me, "You're gay, aren't you? Why don't you just come out and say it?" And I say, "Oh yes, I'm certainly very happy. I love listening to torch songs and wearing pink and trying on make-up or wearing one of Jane's dresses" – but they keep asking! What shall I do?' – *Anon*

Unfortunately, I could not help this reader because I never reply to anonymous letters. However, if you think you can, please send your answers to: 'Is George Happy? c/o Uncle Bungle, London'.

5: The Zen of Zippy

Hello, me again. As I told you all before, I've been very busy since leaving *Rainbow* and have learned a great many things. For instance, in the mid-1990s I became a Buddhist and learned the true meaning of humility, which obviously makes me the smartest one by far. Here are some other things I know a lot about.

Music

As I said before, I am a world-famous DJ, which is great. There's nothing I like better than banging out pumping raves in Ibiza and I like to keep up to date with all the latest vibes, although I do sometimes get the words confused. Here are my top five favourite musical things.

George Michael – Used to be in a band called Wham!, now gone a bit funny … must be something to do with being called George. Also used to play the banjo and sing about what he did while cleaning windows, I think.

The Beatles – Not a lot of people know that The Beatles borrowed all their best ideas from *Rainbow*. For instance, that song 'The Long and Winding Road' is about how

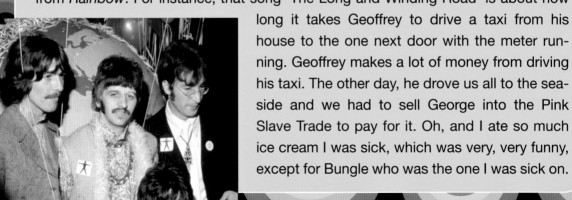

long it takes Geoffrey to drive a taxi from his house to the one next door with the meter running. Geoffrey makes a lot of money from driving his taxi. The other day, he drove us all to the seaside and we had to sell George into the Pink Slave Trade to pay for it. Oh, and I ate so much ice cream I was sick, which was very, very funny, except for Bungle who was the one I was sick on.

Craig David – I like him because he has funny hair and says his name a lot, like I do. I also like Charlotte Church, who has done so much for rock music since her days with Black Sabbath.

Eminem – I really envy him because he gets to play with a chainsaw on stage, whereas I have to make do with scissors and cardboard. He made a great record with a girl called Dido – which is a funny name, although Geoffrey says it would be even funnier with an extra 'l'. I wonder what he means?

'Murder on the Dancefloor' – I like this song, although I've never actually seen anyone murdered on a dancefloor. The girl who sings it has a square head and three names, she's very pretty but I don't fancy her. If you must know, I fancied Emily from *Bagpuss*. I tried to kiss her once, but my zip got caught in her hair and she pulled me around for two whole episodes, but nobody noticed because it was on the BBC. Ha ha!

The Tweenies – The only thing all of us agree about is

how much we hate the Tweenies. They have big heads and they're very ugly, and none of their songs make any sense. I especially hate the purple one. It really worries me that kids today are growing up wanting to be like that. I remember when they all wanted to be pink hippos who liked wearing colourful scarves.

And that's all I have to say about music.

Kid's TV

The other thing I know a lot about is kids' TV, because I invented most of it in 1972. People often ask me, 'Did you get on with the other big stars?' and I say – 'Of course! Everyone liked me and invited me to tea and we all became best of friends.' Here are some stories about them that the tabloids turned down because they weren't strictly true.

Captain Scarlet is not really indestructible. The other day he twisted his ankle and cried like a baby. George eventually offered to kiss it better and when Captain Scarlet refused George followed him home. I'm a bit worried about George.

Magpie – People often ask me about *Magpie* because we worked in the same studio in the 1970s. I liked *Magpie* because it was just like *Blue Peter* except with presenters you actually fancied. I always fancied Jenny but George seemed to like Mick, the one with the big hair. Did I say how worried we all were about George?

Danger Mouse – I don't know what all the fuss is about. He never does anything really dangerous, like eating Marmite or playing 'Pin the tail on the Bungle' or telling Rod, Jane and Freddy not to sing about absolutely everything they do. I heard one the other day called 'Sitting on the Toilet', which is more than I needed to know – that's for sure!

Anyway, I'm off now to open a new supermarket called 'Zips R Us'. I'll pop by later and see how you are.

6: Things We Should Have Said No To

Rainbow merchandising is big business and even though the cast were not entirely happy with some of the products chosen, the sheer demand of our fans ensured a constant supply of videos, annuals, bean toys and socks.

Even so, there are some ideas that should definitely have stayed on the drawing board...

Zippy by Calvin Klein (1979)

Launched at the height of *Rainbow* mania, this men's fragrance with a hint of beef extract failed to catch on with its target audience. The failure was largely put down to the advertising slogan 'It's a lot better than smelling like Bungle ...' and a disastrous '22-for-the-price-of-one!' marketing campaign.

GEOFFREY'S

A-X

OF LONDON

Geoffrey's A-X of London (1997)

In the late 1990s I agreed to endorse this illustrated guide to London, utilizing the famous 'Knowledge' so valued by licensed cabbies. Unfortunately, several tabloids picked up on a few anomalies, including what they called 'unnecessarily long routes between very nearby places' and half the maps overwritten with the message 'Sorry, don't go saath of the river, Petal!'

The idea was later sold to Channel 5 and re-launched as a soap opera.

SUGGESTED ROUTE

TAXI

Rainbow Warrior (1981)

In an inspired leap of wordplay, eco-heroes Greenpeace signed the cast to promote their famous flagship, *Rainbow Warrior*. The launch was planned as a major media event before the ship set sail to scupper French nuclear tests in the South Pacific.

'In retrospect,' said a Greenpeace spokesman, 'letting Bungle drive the boat was just sodding stupid …'

THINGS WE SHOULD HAVE SAID NO TO

What Thimble? (1984)

George was widely agreed to be the one with least commercial savvy in the cast, as this magazine cover proves. Aimed at 'the downwardly mobile seamstress' it sold only three copies, slightly fewer than his other publishing ventures *What Tea Dance?* and *What Doily?*

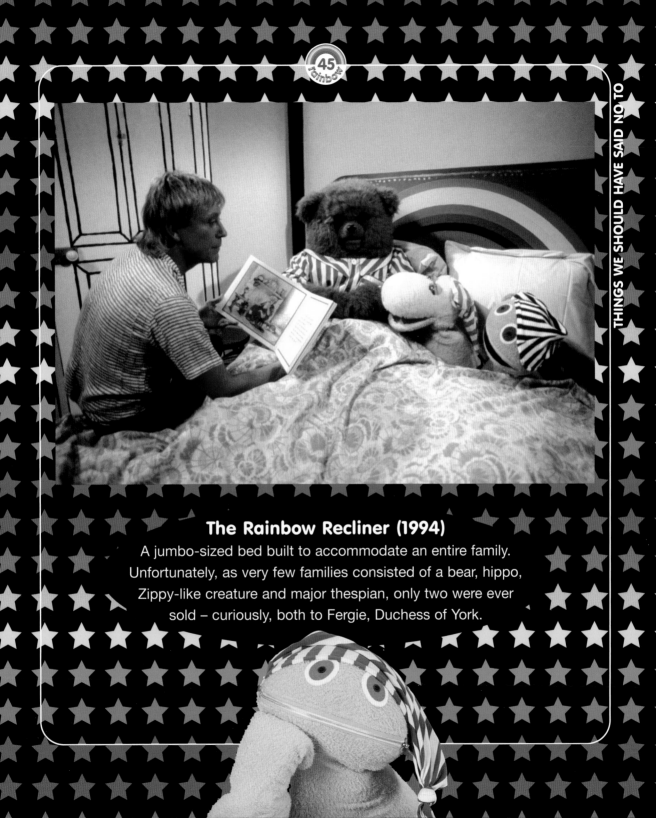

The Rainbow Recliner (1994)

A jumbo-sized bed built to accommodate an entire family. Unfortunately, as very few families consisted of a bear, hippo, Zippy-like creature and major thespian, only two were ever sold – curiously, both to Fergie, Duchess of York.

Motherware (1979)

At first, chain-store Motherware's decision to launch a range of school uniforms based on a hit TV show seemed like a smart move. However, when a tabloid exposed the rising problem of playground bullying, the line was hastily withdrawn.

'In retrospect …' said a spokesman, 'we realized that if you were going to make your child wear matching fluorescent dungarees to school you might as well just duff him up yourself.'

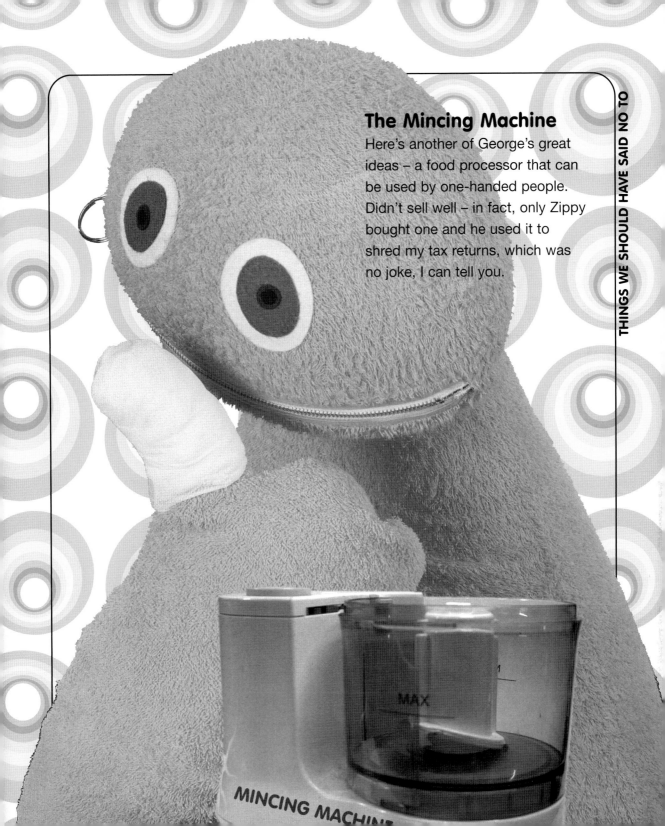

The Mincing Machine

Here's another of George's great ideas – a food processor that can be used by one-handed people. Didn't sell well – in fact, only Zippy bought one and he used it to shred my tax returns, which was no joke, I can tell you.

MINCING MACHINE

MAX

Hippo Flakes (1986)

Promising '300 times the fibre of everything else in your larder put together', Hippo Flakes was designed to catch the wave of US fitness fads. Extensive medical tests later showed it to cause cranial swelling and gigantism in some children.

George's Sounds of the 90s (1999)

Compilation albums were all the rage as the millennium approached, but George's ultimate party megamix performed poorly at the tills.

Ravers were confused by the juxtaposition of Basement Jaxx and The Chemical Brothers with much slower tracks by Bette Midler and Harry Connick Jnr. Eyebrows were also raised when Geri Halliwell's 'It's Raining Men' appeared six times on the same CD.

'I told him it would all turn out wrong …' said a delighted Zippy. 'That's why George is George and I'm a world-famous DJ.'

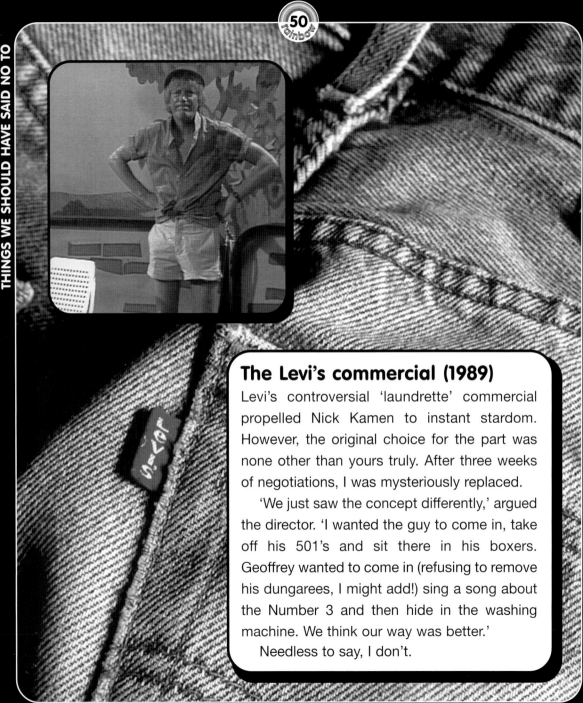

The Levi's commercial (1989)

Levi's controversial 'laundrette' commercial propelled Nick Kamen to instant stardom. However, the original choice for the part was none other than yours truly. After three weeks of negotiations, I was mysteriously replaced.

'We just saw the concept differently,' argued the director. 'I wanted the guy to come in, take off his 501's and sit there in his boxers. Geoffrey wanted to come in (refusing to remove his dungarees, I might add!) sing a song about the Number 3 and then hide in the washing machine. We think our way was better.'

Needless to say, I don't.

Rainbowania (1995)

Although Zippy became quite a whiz-kid entrepreneur, his boldest idea was also our biggest collective loss. Rainbowania was envisaged as an international theme park to rival EuroDisney, costing over £300 million and utilizing a lavish 100-acre site. Unfortunately, due to a poor choice of location (just outside Sarajevo) and an unforgivably greedy entrance fee, in the six months it was open it failed to attract any visitors at all. This fact was concealed from the administrators by Rod, Jane and Freddy allegedly going in and out of the park all day to give an impression of heavy traffic. They were even said to have written a song about it called 'Going Round the Turnstiles' although this, like Rainbowania itself, is increasingly the stuff of legend.

THINGS WE SHOULD HAVE SAID NO TO

7: Talking Rainbow

When a programme runs for twenty years, it invariably affects the language of the day and *Rainbow* was no exception. Curiously, the jargon only took off in under-world circles, where cockney gangsters frequently took to 'Talking Rainbow' in order to confuse their enemies. Here are a few of the more common examples.

doing a bungle

keep it zippy

tone geoff

Doing a Bungle – Speaking or behaving in a manner that causes maximum irritation to those around you. People who do a Bungle usually end up 'in the Thames', 'getting a bit R&F' with the fishes. See also: 'Doing an Ainsley' or 'Doing a Mandelson'.

Tone Geoff – One who suffers fools gladly. As in 'That bloke who manages Westlife – he's a bit tone geoff, innit?'

Keep it Zippy – Originally meaning 'to keep your mouth shut', especially when interrogated by police. As the series wore on, however, it became apparent that Zippy was unable to keep schtum for more than eleven seconds per show, whereupon the phrase came to mean 'being fast or spontaneous'.

Georgian – Flamboyant but slightly out of place. For example, inviting Julian Clary to meet the Pope would be very Georgian indeed.

Easy Virgin – A promise that looks to good to be true. As in, 'Look, trust me and make the commercial – I guarantee no one will think you're just a taxi driver!'

> very georgian

> we need a jane here

Jane – A welcome but deliberate distraction. For example, during every single episode of *Andy Pandy*, nobody questioned why Looby Loo always ran away whenever Teddy appeared. In this instance, the 'Jane' took the form of a catchy theme song about waving goodbye, which distracted us from the felony that probably occurred later when he finally did catch up with her.

Painting Rainbows – Inspiring terror through unpredictable behaviour. E.g. 'So when he refused to pay up we started hanging around his manor for days on end, you know – singing songs and dressing up and stuff. It freaked the geezer out, by the end of the week he was painting rainbows!'

Making Marmite – Making a lot of money through endorsing something you don't actually like. As used by Hollywood superstars advertising hair-care products in foreign countries because they figure no one of any importance will ever see them. Also politicians who work for arms manufacturers.

Over the Rainbow

Rainbow was on the air for twenty years, but did you know it was originally intended to be a hard-hitting current affairs programme? Relive those wonderful days with this board game – pick your favourite character, throw the dice and head for the Rainbow.

1979
You discover that Jim Davidson has been doin[g] impressions of you on T[V]. Go back 5 places and lo[se] all your street credibilit[y].

1978
Geoffrey offers you a lift in his taxi. Lose 2 turns and £35 for the half-mile journey.

1972
ITV commissions you to do a show, possibly News at Ten. Advance 2 places.

1977
George stops off to go shopping at Vivienne Westwood's on the Kings Road and spends the entire production budget on ear-rings. Go back to the start.

1973
George decides not to join The Beach Boys and hooks up with you instead. Take an extra turn.

1976
Bungle is voted 'Hunk of the Week' by the readers of TV Times, narrowly beating Magnum star Tom Selleck. Advance 1 square but miss a turn while you check your eyesight.

1974
Robin Day leaves the show after refusing to wear dungarees. ITV hires Geoffrey and changes the format. Advance 2 places.

1975
Zippy ruins a whole episode by refusing to come out of his dressing room. Miss a turn.

1980
The BBC cancels Watch with Mother and your ratings go through the roof. Take an extra turn.

1981
Jane is feeling unwell and has to be replaced by Margaret Thatcher. Rod and Freddy refuse to play with her. Miss a turn.

1982
Geoffrey tries to join a rock band called The Police, putting on the application form that he used to work on Z-Cars. Move back 3 places.

1983
George is arrested for camping outside Wembley Arena before a Chippendales concert. Throw a 6 to continue.

1984
Bungle gets beaten up by the Mr Men, and has to go to hospital. Throw a 6 to continue.

1985
Zippy sues the aliens from the Cadbury's Smash commercial. 'But your honour,' he says, 'they stole my entire act!' Miss a turn.

1986
George opens a fashion boutique called 'Hipposexual' – it loses a small fortune. Go back 10 places.

1987
In pay negotiations for a new series, the cast demands £1 million per show. ITV says no. They agree to continue doing it for more tea and jammy dodgers. Move on two spaces.

1988
Rod, Jane and Freddy write a song about Rainbow merchandising. It's called 'I Can Spell a Goldmine'. Move on five places.

1989
After years of public denial, Zippy is discovered unconscious in his hotel room having OD'd on Marmite. Miss a turn.

1990
Bungle throws a tea party to bring peace to the Middle East. Nobody shows up. Miss a turn.

1991
The Rainbow theme tune becomes an Ibiza summer hit – move on two places.

1992
ITV has an attack of madness and cancels the show. Go back to the start.

END
Hooray! After twenty years you make it to the end of the Rainbow. Sadly, there is no gold – Zippy got there first.

8: Where's Bungle?

Bungle loves playing hide and seek,
but can you spot where he's hiding?
(Clue: He's about three times the size
of everything else in the picture.)

9: The Best Songs U Never Heard

Long before the Tweenies, there was Rod, Jane and Freddy, pop troubadours with a song for every occasion. Who could forget their classic 'If it wasn't for the cow, where would you be right now?' written a full twenty years before Foot and Mouth brought the farming community to its knees. Prophetic stuff, indeed.

Castle

RJF (as they were known to their fans) were fiercely proud of their material, rehearsing constantly and taking especial care over the lyrics. Consequently, although other writers tried to write songs for them, they were never performed.

Here are a few of our favourites that never made it on to the show. Feel free to invent your own tunes and sing along.

You can never have too many E's

There's one in Red but two in Tree
Three in Geese and four in Eeeek!
You can have as many as five in Greek.
The truth of the matter is:
You can never have too many E's …

(Rod)
Oh E is the letter we love the best
(Freddy)
It's much more cool than all the rest
(Jane)
You can take one E and another will follow
(All together)
Let's go find some E's tomorrow!

I can see your jugs

(Jane)
I've been visiting Mr Cow
I've got cream for my breakfast now
But in case someone tries to steal it first
I'll hide these jugs till the end of the verse

(Freddy)
Hey, I can see your jugs from here!
(Rod)
Oh, can I see those jugs up near?
(Jane)
Oh no you can't, they're both for me
Unless you want a cup of tea.

World problems

Oh there's not enough food to feed the poor
And global warming is an awful bore.
There's fear and pain when economies crumble.
But all we can think about is …
Oh dear, here's Bungle!

There's Third World debt and declining trade,
And little bitty kids being sold as slaves,
There's mass destruction of reefs and jungles.
But our main concern is
Avoiding Bungle.

(Chorus)
He's soft and brown and his eyes are sleepy
But why'd he have to look so creepy?

Let's try swinging

We all like playing in the park
(Yes we do, Yes we do)
There's slides and climbs and lots of grass
(Yes there is, Yes there is)
But there's one thing that we haven't tried
That's why we can't stop singing,
It makes you feel all good inside
So let's try swinging!

Up and down and down and up
Swinging's the life for me.
Down and up, up and down
Makes me happy as can be.

Things you shouldn't do

There's lots of things that you can do
To pass the time if you're feeling blue
But here's a few that you really shouldn't try
They may sound fun, and they may sound cool.
But take our word – you would be a fool
So listen now and we'll spell them out for you.

Oh …

Don't go killing things
By ripping off their wings
Don't sit on your mates
And guff until they shake
Don't run off with cash
That loan-sharks may want back
And please don't sleep around
With girls who charge in pounds.

Now wasn't that true?
And wasn't that fun?
But don't go yet
We're not quite done

Oh …

Don't try sniffing glue
It's really not good for you
Don't go stealing cars
You might end up behind bars
And don't rub out your mates
With razor-wire or snakes.
And don't burn down some shops
They'll only call the cops.

'That was a funny song, wasn't it? But let's go look in the Scrapbook now …'

10: Bungle's Scrapbook

It's thirty years since we started together on *Rainbow*, and what busy lives we've all had! Some of us did amazing things, some of us sat around at home pretending to be Liberace, but we always took great photos to remember it by.

So take a trip with me down memory lane and learn about all the amazing things we got up to off-screen.

Well, here we all are doing one of our many university gigs. *Rainbow* is still amazingly popular with students, who find watching our shows on video fills the gap nicely between eating kebabs, stealing essays off the internet and sleeping with people they hardly know.

Long before *Rainbow*, Geoffrey was busy as a bee. Here you can see him on an errand for NASA, delivering two very important passengers to the lunar surface in 1969. Best of all, he kept the meter running …

'That'll be $23 million and $2.50 for the bags, guv!' he said.

Isn't Geoffrey funny?

Awwww … wasn't I sweet? As you can see, I was quite a large baby. In fact my mother was in labour for so long it started in the heart of the Peruvian rainforest and finished in a brand new shopping mall just outside Lima.

Radio 1 DJ Chris Moyles has been a lifelong *Rainbow* fan and invited the cast on his show in 1999. Unusually, George was rude throughout, repeatedly questioning the DJ's parentage and on one occasion biting him in the backside.

'I was a bit upset,' he admitted later. 'And I never did like Chris Evans ...'

SCRAPBOOK

Everyone remembers Zippy impersonating Cherie Blair on BBC1's *Dead Ringers* – but he's been a stunt double for many stars, including Julia Roberts and Steve Tyler from Aerosmith. Earlier this year there were even rumours of a secret romance with Sophie Ellis-Bextor, although when you consider what the children would have looked like, it's a good thing they were only rumours.

+

=

One of George's many obsessions is *Big Brother*, which he tried to get on to on more than one occasion. Here he is having an argument with Jade, the one from *Big Brother 3* who thought Birmingham had a beach. ''Ere, you're a 'ippo!' she told him. 'That's a larrf, innit?' George was apparently too traumatized to speak for several days after this.

SCRAPBOOK

Recently released government files revealed the surprising story of Zippy being recruited as a spy in the mid-1980s. MI5 felt his huge popularity might open doors for them, especially in eastern Europe. His supervisor's notes tell a different story.

'The Warsaw assignment was a disaster. Agent Zippy was arrested at the airport after putting down 'International Spy' as his occupation. He then proceeded to blurt out everything he knew about the agency, all his contacts, even the phone numbers of other agents. Most annoyingly, he was not being interrogated at the time, just making small-talk with a customs official.'

Unfortunately this is one we like to forget. George was invited on *So Graham Norton* and got a bit carried away, first chasing Graham round and round the sofa and then bursting into an emotional ten-minute rendition of his favourite song, an Indian love lyric entitled 'Pale hands I love ...' When the host tried to remove him from the set, I naturally leapt to his aid.

In the resulting scuffle, 132 members of the audience were slightly hurt as well as twenty-three viewers. For reasons still unknown, Geoffrey was the only one arrested even though he was out of the country at the time.

SCRAPBOOK

Another proud moment for us was being selected to sing Britain's Eurovision entry in the mid-1980s. Our song was called 'Bang Bang Bang' and was written by the same guy who wrote 'Boom Bang a Bang' for Lulu and 'Bang Bang' for B.A. Robertson. We came second last, one place above Italy's entry 'E Boingy Boingy Boingy Boingy Boingy!'

Here I am in 1978 entering the Miss Thames TV beauty pageant because Zippy dared me to. I came second last, just above the HMS *Belfast*. I did, however, go on to be Miss East Germany from 1979–1983.

Even while busy with *Rainbow*, Geoffrey always kept his acting career going. Here you can see him as Paulie 'The Trousers' Castanetta in *Goodfellas* and Colin Firth's brother R.C. D'Arcy in *Pride and Prejudice*. Controversially, both roles were cut after his co-stars complained of being upstaged.

'The kid clearly had talent ...' admitted Pesci later. 'But nobody slaps me around on-screen because I forget the words to "Humpty Dumpty" – d'ya hear me – nobody!!!'

But of course Geoffrey's favourite hobby has always been driving, and he's very good at it! Here he is beating Michael Schumacher at the Brazilian Grand Prix, although ITV's in-car microphone captured the full story even better.

Passenger: ' … and Terminal 4 is where, exactly?'

Geoffrey: 'Nahhh worries, china – this is a short cut!'

11: Jamming With Zippy

Everybody loves the *Rainbow* theme song – but Zippy likes it the best.
Why not sing along with him?

'Oh no, Zippy, you're ruining the song!'

'Up above the streets and houses,
Rainbow climbing high
Everyone can see it smiling
Over the sky

Diddle diddle diddle diddle-ee
Etc.

Hello children my name is Zippy
I'm the famous one
I've got far more cash than the others
That's why I'm having fun …

Diddle diddle diddle diddle-ee
Etc.

No one in the world fancies Bungle,
But everyone loves Jane,
Rod and Freddy more than the others …
George is a total pain …

I refuse to eat any Marmite
But I'll do the ad,
Send the money straight to my agent
That really makes him glad …

Diddle diddle diddle diddle-ee
Etc.

'Geoffrey! Zippy is changing all the words …'

'Right, that's quite enough of that!'

zzzzz

'Paint the whole world with a RAINBOW!!!'

Mmmmph

12: Fan Fiction

Internet users may be familiar with the legion of short stories, movies and poems that get written about famous TV characters. This is known as 'fan fiction' and, like any cult show, *Rainbow* has its own share of crazy fans who like to let their imaginations run wild.

Here is one of the better attempts at *Rainbow* fan fiction, posted on the internet by someone claiming to be a 23-year-old cyber-genius named KrYPToNiTE. We think it shows a lot of promise, although when George Lucas finds out someone's going to get sued …

(NB: watch out for the bit when his mum walks in the room …)

An extract from 'Episode 5: The Empire Strikes Bungle':

As the Millennium Hawk emerged from subspace it was immediately clear something was wrong. It was quiet, too damned quiet for a sector of space which should have been crawling with Raidellian bounty hunters eager for a quick kill.

But G–Solo knew they were round here somewhere, hiding, waiting for their mark, and if they were looking for a fight they had come to the right roughneck.

'Chewie,' he snapped at his headset. 'Get your furry butt up here right now … this plasma conduit doesn't mend itself …'

That slip of the tongue annoyed him more than he cared to admit. Chewie had been a legend, a sharp–shooting fur–ball that every man wanted at his side and no pilot wanted in his rear–view mirror. Chewie could fix a drive in three hours and hit the eye of an Imperial storm–trooper eight times out of ten. Chewie was a sidekick to be proud of, right up to the moment he sacrificed his life for his friend at the battle of Nabooboo Prime.

No, they don't make 'em like Chewie every day. Damn, he missed that guy!

'I've got fizzy drinks here ... if anyone's asking,' said Bungle, appearing at the portal wearing an apron and carrying a tray. 'And sandwiches too, if I only knew where George had put the bread ... Hmmm ... I wonder where it is? Can you see it anywhere?'

And they don't make 'em like his new replacement either ...

'Forget that, bud!' he snapped. 'We're going to have Delta Wings up our ass in about three minutes and we're dead in the water here ... Now get me a frag-wrench and strip out those diagnostic panels!'

'Hmmmm,' continued Bungle, scratching his head. 'Perhaps the bread is in that box over in the corner ... Shall I look over there? Oooh, shall I?'

G-Solo muttered something under his breath and roughly pushed the Wookie-wannabe aside, showering cherry cola across the already untidy control room. If you want to do something right, do it yourself ...

The engine room was still showering

sparks and hot as hell. Hardly surprising when the back-up generators take a direct hit from a Federation Mothership. The Millennium Hawk might have broken every speed record in the book, but when Darth Zippy wants you dead that's what usually happens. He knew they were lucky to have made it this far.

The secret was to focus on one problem at a time, and right now the problem was why the hell had the LightDrive cut out in the middle of a Q-Jump? This one item cost more than most pilots earn in a year and it never broke down without a damn good reason

G-Solo took a deep breath and squatted in front of the massive engine

casing, knowing he could open it to find a plasma-fire which would strip his skin away in five nano-seconds. At best, he would find fried circuitry and a repair job that would take six weeks in dry-dock. Nervously, he prized his fingers round the back of the facia panel and pulled hard.

'Hello Geoffrey ...' said George, waving.

'Hello George,' said G-Solo. 'What are you doing in the LightDrive?'

'I was hiding the bread from Bungle. Look, here it is!'

He should have killed him there and then ... it would have been so easy. So what if he was a Jedi Master? So what if he knew the secrets of the Force? He had destroyed a 3 million-credit engine with a loaf of sliced bread – wasn't that reason enough?

'Look, just take it and go ...' he sighed, surveying the damage.

George grinned and wobbled off in the direction of Luke Skywalker's private quarters. G–Solo pushed his head deep into the engine core and prayed for a miracle ...

'Getting dirty again, I see ...' said a voice

He looked up. As if didn't have enough distractions already.

Princess Jane had showered and changed clothes. She smelt of rosewater ... which he liked in a woman. And she

looked ... well, like no princess he had ever seen before: straight blonde hair; pert, full figure; a pair of hips you ought-ta take up skiing to explore, and an attitude that said 'If you can't ride the pony, don't buy the saddle.'

'So what, if I'm dirty ...' he snarled, standing and leaning towards her. 'You like dirty ... you need men like me ... men who mess up your cosy idea of correctness ...'

'Stop that ...' she said, pulling her hand away.

'Why?' he whispered, leaning closer.

'Because I might like it ...' she breathed.

She melted into his strong lips like sherbet ... all that fake nobility disappearing in a line of kisses that arched from her neck and over the mounds of her perfect ...

And THAT was what I did in Spring Break ... Like I said, the Rockies are one fun place to visit and all my friends thought it was really cool that we didn't meet any Indians ...

Jason Munroe – aged twelve

To be continued ...

13: So You Want To Be In Rainbow?

A lot of people say to me, 'Geoffrey, how did you get to be in *Rainbow* in the first place?'

This is a very good question, because believe me it wasn't easy. *Rainbow* was the *Pop Idol* of its day, with hundreds of star-struck hopefuls fighting for a place on what would be the biggest and best show on television.

It started in London with a series of gruelling rehearsals and auditions to whittle us down to around twelve finalists. Competition in all the categories was strong, but the role of presenter was the most hectic of all, eventually boiling down to a tense final audition between me, Sir John Gielgud, David Bowie, and the guy who played Blakey in *On the Buses*.

It was then that the producers hit us with our final test – a questionnaire designed to find out which one of us was best suited to the job. Naturally, I picked the right answers, got the job and the rest is history, but by sheer chance I found the original questionnaire the other day and here it is for you all to play along with.

Are you sitting comfortably? Good, then we'll begin …

Question 1
You are given £25,000 to spend on a wardrobe of new clothes. What do you buy?

a) A tasteful selection of designer labels, from the likes of Yves St Laurent and Hugo Boss. If there's any money left over, spend it on a flashy sports car.

b) A few hipper numbers from Carnaby Street, paying special attention to the fabrics. If there's any left, spend it on a trendy haircut that the kids will want to copy.

c) An assortment of jeans and jumpers in colours so bright it would give Marc Bolan a migraine. If there's any left, spend it all on funny hats.

Question 2
You are at a party, when someone makes a pass at your girlfriend. What do you do?

a) Give the guy a good kung-fu kicking, using any or all weapons at your disposal. If he refuses to back down, run him over with your car.

b) Try to have a mature discussion with him, explaining that as a highly paid TV presenter there's no way he could compete with you even if he tried.

c) Dance around him, singing songs. If this doesn't work, dance around someone else.

Question 3

ITV cuts your production budget so something will have to be dropped from the show. What goes?

a) Bungle – let's face it, he is a bit odd, isn't he?

b) The lavish Ziegfeld Follies number that George wanted to do, where The Chippendales carry him down a big staircase and throw him into a fountain.

c) What's a production budget anyway?

Question 4

You are offered a part in a Hollywood blockbuster which includes a lengthy love scene with Sharon Stone. Do you ...

a) Accept the part immediately.

b) Insist on script changes so you can keep your clothes on throughout.

c) Stick with *Rainbow*, it's regular work and easier on the knees.

Question 5

You are asked to fill in a questionnaire but it soon becomes patently obvious that the answer is always c). What do you do?

a) Refuse to take part in so foolish an exercise and storm out of the audition vowing to sack your agent.

b) Suspect a double bluff and continue to answer each question as honestly as you can.

c) Answer c).

Scoring:

5 points for each correct answer.

Answers:

1:c 2:c 3:c 4:c 5:c

So how did you fare?

0–5 points – You may well have a perfectly good career in retailing or possibly chartered accountancy but a children's TV presenter you ain't! Try to loosen up and not take yourself so seriously.

6–20 points – Not bad, with a bit of typecasting there may be hope for you yet. We suggest a spot on *Play Away* until you're ready for the big time.

21–25 points – Congratulations! Not only are you the presenter we're looking for but we always planned on calling him Geoffrey anyway. By the way, do you mind starting now, because we're on the air in half an hour!

14: Making Things Better with Bungle

Hello – It's me again.

Another great thing about *Rainbow* is all the terrific things we made on the show. Of course, I came up with most of them myself – and believe me, it wasn't easy. For instance, we had loads of things we wanted to make from washing-up liquid bottles, but apparently *Blue Peter* had the copyright so we had to make do with shoeboxes instead.

Anyway, here are a few of our favourite things. Remember, you can make them using mainly everyday household objects. And if you can't find something, Geoffrey will always help you find it. The other day Zippy lost his patience and was in danger of losing his marbles too, but Geoffrey said he found them after locking me in a cupboard for three days.

Isn't Geoffrey funny?

1 - Ferrari F1 Sports car

1) First find a big shoebox, and carefully cut holes in all four corners.

2) Attach four cotton reels to the box, using thin wooden skewers. Be careful, the ends may be sharp!

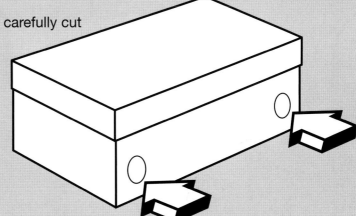

3) Paint the whole thing red.

4) Attach a Ferrari 051 V10 engine, preferably with a semi-automatic sequential electronically controlled longitudinal gearbox, with limited slip differential.

5) There – now go for a drive. Oh, you'll need a driver …

2 - David Coulthard

Stand the shoebox
on its end.

3 - Big Brother live simulator

1) Stand shoebox on side, remove lid.

2) Watch closely for up
to twelve hours at a
time. If something
interesting occurs,
you're on the
wrong channel.

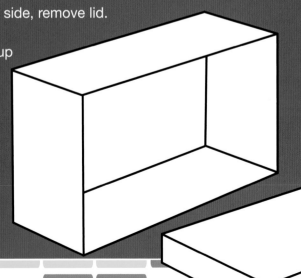

4 - A tactical nuclear device

1) Find a shoebox and half fill it with soil from the garden.

2) Add a generous quantity of refined Uranium 235. (NB: Uranium 238 won't do.)

3) Tape down the lid. Remember, this is your only containment for the fusion reaction, so make it good and firm.

4) Ask Zippy to shake the box vigorously until something happens. Stand well back.

5 - How to keep George occupied for hours

1) Take a shoebox.

2) Fill it with glitter, earrings and felt.

3) Play music.

4) Add more glitter.

6 - Phil Mitchell from EastEnders

1) Stand shoebox on its end.

2) Paint face on lid.

3) Occasionally pick a fight with it.

HIYA!

NUMBER 13 • FEBRUARY 1995 • £16.99

INTERNATIONAL MAGAZINE OF THE YEAR

ZIPPY – STRANGELY QUIET

EXCLUSIVE

GEORGE

REVEALS ALL ABOUT HIS EXOTIC LIFESTYLE

BUNGLE COMES CLEAN ABOUT CROSS-DRESSING

INSIDE GEORGE'S BOUDOIR

15: George's Boudoir

In early 1995, George invited the popular magazine *Hiya!* to his home to discuss his exotic style and very personal tastes. It was generally considered to be a mistake, reinforcing a widely held conception that he had some serious issues to deal with. Here is the article as it appeared:

GEORGE EXCLUSIVE

He's certainly come a long way since *Rainbow* but George the Hippo just loves the sumptuous pad in Holland Park he shares with the rest of the cast. With its elegant Georgian façade and ample garden the reclusive star showed us around the suite of rooms he personally decorated to make it feel more homely.

'Oh yes … I love it here …' he tells us. 'Even better now I stripped out all that original wood panelling and painted it pink.'

With five bedrooms and an indoor mud-pool, this des-res doesn't come cheap. It was valued at nearly £2 million earlier this year, but George insists he will never move, even though his latest TV series *Who Wants to be a Hippopotamus?* was recently refused syndication in the US on account of its flagrant cruelty to zoo-keepers. So can he really still afford to live so opulently?

'Oh, yes …' he replies, 'I'm very careful with my money. In fact, only last week I invested my entire fortune in a company called "Ratners" (I think they make pet food or something) so I'm sure I'll be set up for life now … Besides, where else would I keep all my favourite things?'

George is a prolific collector of fine art – specializing in what the experts call 'Superficial Kitsch'. Upstairs we are allowed to see his extensive collections of high-heeled shoes, earrings and

'Yes, I keep meaning to come out of the closet but I never seem to get round to it …'

a closet full of stuff he borrowed from Jane and forgot to return – which is definitely one of his favourite rooms, judging by the amount of time he spends in there …

'Yes, I keep meaning to come out of the closet but I never seem to get round to it …' he admits

George's bedroom is possibly the most unusual room in the house, and has become a virtual shrine to his favourite stars. In the corner stands a white baby-grand piano once owned by Liberace, on the dresser Judy Garland's slippers (not the ones from *The Wizard of Oz*, the quilted size-eights she wore while in rehab) and one of the walls contains every single hit single ever released by Bonnie Tyler.

'I've got them both …' he grins. 'But my favourite is "Total Eclipse of the Heart", which was written by the guy who did Meat Loaf … which reminds me, I'm soooo hungry.'

As we settle down to a sumptuous breakfast of Mango Juice and Crunchy-Nut Pigmies, it's immediately apparent how far George has come from his days in an African swamp.

'I've had a wonderful life … and I owe it all to *Rainbow*,' he confides. 'In fact, when we start the new series, they've promised to let me sing "MacArthur Park" and something from *Cabaret*. I get to dress up and everything!'

At this point, we feel obliged to remind him that *Rainbow* has been taken off the air and there is a strong possibility it will never return.

'Oh, they're just saying that,' he laughs. 'It'll be back – *Rainbow* will run forever and we'll always be friends.'

Although the rest of the cast are currently away pursuing solo projects they clearly still have a heavy influence in his life. In fact, there's no escaping the giant painting of Bungle which hangs above the fireplace.

'Damien Hirst did that …' he smiles. 'He really wanted to saw him in half and preserve him in formaldehyde, but I said that would never catch on and so he did me a nice watercolour instead. Geoffrey offered me a fiver for it – so I've made money already!'

One question we cannot resist asking is how they really get on together – after all, it must be a strain both working and living together for over twenty years. Once again, our host is unstinting in his praise.

'We just like being together …' he beamed. 'Of course, it's a bit much having to share a bed, partly because Geoffrey talks in his sleep but mainly because Rod, Jane and Freddy sing in theirs. But every day is an adventure and what could be better than that … apart from sharing a house with Boyzone, of course!'

As I leave him, George is busy on the phone discussing new projects with his agent. One thing he is clearly excited about is an upcoming audition for a new pop band, which should finally allow him show off his full range of talents as a singer and dancer.

'It's top secret …' he whispers. 'But I hear they've got a posh one, a baby one, a scary one, a sporty one and now they're looking for a plump one who wears too much make-up – now who could do that better than me?'

We wish him well …

'Of course, it's a bit much having to share a bed, partly because Geoffrey talks in his sleep but mainly because Rod, Jane and Freddy sing in theirs.'

16: The People versus Rainbow

Possibly the darkest chapter in the history of *Rainbow* happened in 1989 when concerned parents at a Hampshire comprehensive school launched a class-action suit against the show claiming they were unfit role-models for children. The entire cast was duly summoned to the Old Bailey to defend their work and reputations in the full glare of media attention.

The *Guardian* took up the story …
' … at this stage, Humphrey Barker QC played extracts to the court from an episode of *Rainbow*, circa 1988.

'"And so I put it to you, George …" he began, "that you have never actually been in outer space, and yet we have just heard you saying on repeated occasions that the moon is made of cheese … Do you feel it is acceptable to mislead children in this fashion?"

'"But it is …" protested a tearful George from the witness box. "Geoffrey told me so, and he knows everything …"

'"And how do you feel about your decision to wear earrings in this and other episodes? Do you not feel it encourages the young to experiment with cross-dressing?"

'"Oh yes …" replied George, "I get so cross dressing sometimes I don't wear any clothes at all."

'"In fact, you're naked right now in this very witness box, aren't you?" pressed Barker

'At this point, George began to get emotional. Sensing a legal ambush, Geoffrey stood up and began doing a little dance around the courtroom – as he often did on the show. He was forcefully ejected by officials along with Bungle, who despite not joining in was felt to be scaring the jury by looking at them in a funny way. George was excused to allow him time to stop crying and Zippy took the stand.

'"You are Zippy, are you not – a DJ and popular children's entertainer?"

'" … er … no I am not," replied Zippy, "and I deny having anything to do with this programme or anyone else here."

'"But we have video evidence of you appearing on at least 300 shows …"

'"That's not me … I deny it – and I have proof …"

'At this point Zippy began distributing photographs showing him on various beaches in funny hats which were entered as evidence of him having been a resident of Ibiza for the past twenty-five years. The prosecution seemed unconvinced.

'"So who is this character we see on the tapes and indeed in a commercial for Marmite? It certainly looks like you …"

'"I have no idea …" replied Zippy. "It could be Cherie Blair …"

'"I put it to you that you know exactly who this is …" urged Barker.

'"No, I put it to you," replied Zippy.

'"I repeat … I put it to you …"

'"No, I put it to you …"

'"I'm sorry?"

'" … No I'm sorry, and I put it to you …"

'This continued for twenty minutes, with Zippy increasingly amused by the game, but the judge became so aggravated he ordered his testimony to be struck from the record.

'As the trial entered its third day, Rod, Jane and Freddy took the stand together and Barker moved in for the kill.

'"So do you deny …" he continued, 'that Jane was patently too attractive to be seen in a mini-skirt on children's television? Do you also deny that you have encouraged a nation of children to wear brightly coloured dungarees, taking liberties with a highly impressionable audience and limiting them to careers as social workers?"

'This was the crucial prosecution gambit and how they answered was sure to determine the eventual verdict. To a hushed court, they rose as one to give their answer.

'"Actually, we know a song about this …" they said.

'Three verses later, the prosecution's case collapsed in disarray.

'It was widely agreed to be a very good song indeed …'

MING SPRING 2004

ENDUS PRESENTS

IN TECHNICOLOUR (IF AVAILABLE)

rainbow

(18)

HE MOVIE

EYMOUR HOFFMAN • MICHELLE PFEIFFER • WILL SMITH

asta la Vista, Bungle!'

TURING 'ZIP AROUND MY HEART' BY CELINE DION

17: Rainbow, the Movie

'It was a time of heroes, a time when one man decided to take a stand against the networks. A ratings-killing machine sent back to change history – and no damn puppet was going to stand in his way.

Tom Cruise IS Geoffrey ...
In RAINBOW: THE SEARCH FOR BUNGLE.
And remember: in Kids TV no one can hear you swear ...'

People have been talking about a *Rainbow* movie since the early 1970s, when Francis Ford Coppola first approached Bungle to play Fredo Corleone in *The Godfather*. Sadly, this was prevented by contractual obligations, but ideas for a script continued to circulate Hollywood for several years after. In this time, various storylines were suggested and rejected by the cast, who were notoriously protective as to how their characters would be portrayed. Early plans for a thriller (scripted by David Mamet), a teen slasher film and even an erotic comedy were summarily rejected. However in 1981 production did finally begin on *Raging Bear*, directed by Martin Scorsese.

Within weeks it was clear there were major artistic differences.

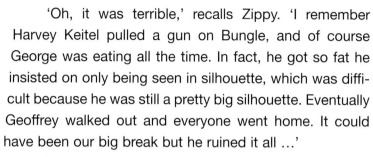

'Oh, it was terrible,' recalls Zippy. 'I remember Harvey Keitel pulled a gun on Bungle, and of course George was eating all the time. In fact, he got so fat he insisted on only being seen in silhouette, which was difficult because he was still a pretty big silhouette. Eventually Geoffrey walked out and everyone went home. It could have been our big break but he ruined it all …'

Naturally, Geoffrey sees things differently.

'It didn't make any sense, darling. Here I was, a classically trained actor and I was expected to do the most ridiculous things. For instance, there was this scene in the warehouse, when Keitel has George tied to a chair and he's about to cut off one of his ears, and they expected me to come on in purple dungarees and sing, "Stuck in the Middle with You" – I mean, come ON – is this the reason I went to RADA???'

Tired of dealing with egos which were inflated even by Hollywood standards, negotiations broke down and the cast found themselves black-listed in the movie world. It proved to be a dark time for all involved.

'I try not to think about it …' says an emotional George. 'I was originally supposed to do *Grease* with John Travolta but they said I couldn't squeeze into the costumes and got Olivia Newton-John instead. Actually, I think she was very good, although she could have done with losing a few pounds – but I'm not bitter.'

The big breakthrough came in 1992, coincidentally the year Rainbow's twenty-year run on the small screen ended. While visiting Britain, Tom Cruise was mistaken for a toddler and locked up for several hours in a crèche. After enduring non-stop children's television he eventually escaped and on his

return to America bought the movie rights to *Rainbow*. The project was very much alive again.

'He knew the moment he saw it …' recalls a close friend of the actor. '*Rainbow* had all the elements he was looking for in a movie. It had emotional intensity, a huge cult following, great characters, but above all a cast who were almost exactly the same height as he was. Of course, there was one major problem, and it had to be sorted out before anything else could happen.'

That problem was Geoffrey, seen by many viewers as an essential part of the show but also the character Cruise was adamant he would play himself.

'I AM this guy!' he insisted at a press conference in Cannes. 'I know how he thinks, I know where he comes from, I feel his torment. Geoffrey is a rebel, he's sick of all the crap and he wants out. Once the fans see me in the role, I know they'll understand.'

Although Geoffrey was kept on as a script consultant, he is now widely rumoured to be planning a class-action lawsuit against the producers along with the rest of the original cast whose subsequent sacking was attributed to 'artistic differences'. As a result, the part of Bungle will be played by Michelle Pfeiffer, George by Phillip Seymour Hoffman, and Zippy by Will Smith.

Finally scheduled for a release in spring 2004, the movie boasts a $70 million budget and state-of the art special effects. The plot sees Geoffrey going back in time to prevent the events which led to the cancellation of *Rainbow* in 1992.

'It's a 21st-century blockbuster for all the family,' said a spokesman for the studio. 'And I'm telling you, Tom has never looked taller!'

The theme song, 'Zip around my Heart' will be performed by Celine Dion.

18: Our Favourite Adventure (part 2)

As you may recall from page 11, Evil Zippy has been brought to life and seems intent on causing chaos wherever he goes.
Oh no!

As soon as he got back to the house, Evil Zippy began weaving his magic spells. First of all, he turned Bungle into a ballerina ...

Then he made Geoffrey ham it up something rotten.

Zippy, meanwhile, had
moved in with Ernie Wise.

And George had been turned into a
big girl. Which was easier than you
might think.

In fact, strange things continued
to happen all morning, and no one
could explain why until …

'Ha ha! For too long have I been overlooked
and undervalued. I was always the smart
one around here, the cool one, the one the
advertisers loved. But did I get the credit?
Of course not. But now you will see the full
extent of Evil Zippy's power!

'Look, I can even make Bungle significantly
less attractive from one episode to the next.'

'So get ready,' sneered Evil Zippy, 'because now you will all suffer like no one except a Channel 5 viewer has ever suffered before!' Oh no, could this be the end for Rainbow?

'Good morning sleepyheads – so what shall we do today?'

'Oh my word,' said Bungle. 'It was all a terrible dream!'

'Well, thank goodness for that,' add Zippy, rubbing his eyes. 'Although it w a lot of fun being evil. You get all the best lines!'

'He's got a point, you know ...' add Geoffrey, phoning his agent.

Only George looked strangely sad.

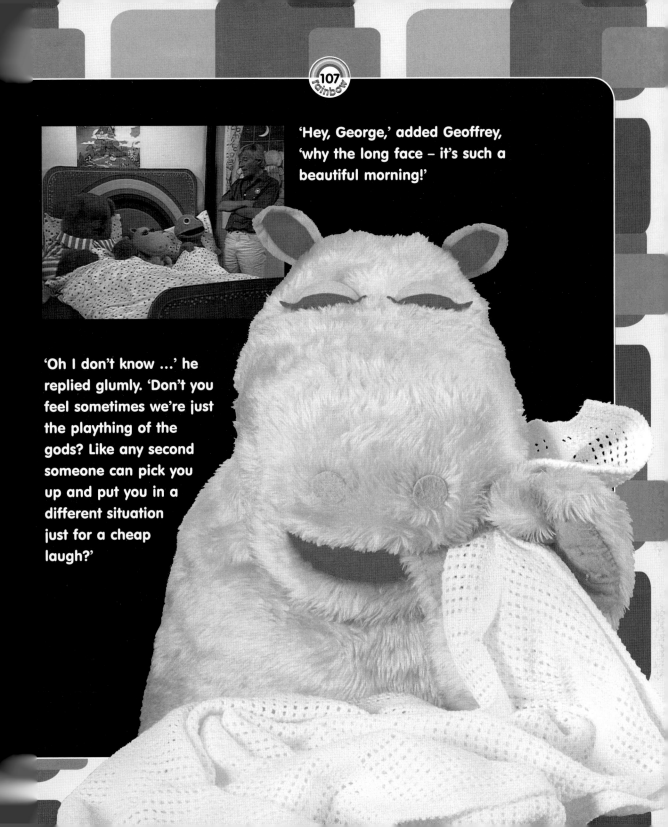

'Hey, George,' added Geoffrey, 'why the long face – it's such a beautiful morning!'

'Oh I don't know ...' he replied glumly. 'Don't you feel sometimes we're just the plaything of the gods? Like any second someone can pick you up and put you in a different situation just for a cheap laugh?'

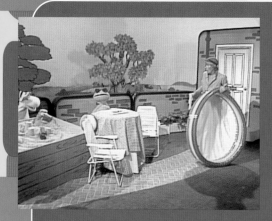

'What on earth do you mean, George?' asked Geoffrey, who appeared to be carrying a very large diaphragm.

'I agree,' said Bungle. 'Who would want to make fun of us?'

'So that's settled then,' agreed Zippy. 'We think you should just cheer up, George, and stop taking it all so seriously. Everybody loves us, and that's the way it always will be.'

And so that's exactly what they did. And five minutes later they all sat down in the garden for a picnic and did what they all loved best: sang a little song of celebration of the end of another wonderful day.

And this is how it went. Why not join in?

'Sing a song of Rainbow
A pocket full of change
Four and twenty actors
Acting very strange.
When the book was over
The readers all said.
'Isn't this a fitting place
To knock it on the head?'
And so it was ...

Well, I'm afraid that's all we've got time for now.
Why not see if you can make up a funny story out
of old video clips? Or maybe get your own kids'
show on ITV for twenty years, if you think it's so
bleeding easy! And we'll see you all very soon.

'Byeeeeee!'

Appendix:
The story so far ...

Rainbow came about in the early 1970s, just as two important changes were taking place in children's television. Firstly there was colour TV, launched in 1969 but only now overtaking black-and-white ownership. The second was *Sesame Street*, newly imported from the US and arguably the first pre-school show to make colour a central part of its appeal.

Impressed by the new interloper and after years of being denied a time slot to challenge the BBC's *Watch with Mother*, ITV decided to mount a rival. The task was handed to Thames Television, then one of ITV's biggest producers. Rather than simply poaching a BBC name, they turned to Pamela Lonsdale, a young producer previously responsible for an acclaimed adaptation of *The Lion the Witch and the Wardrobe* but better known for drama than entertainment.

'I was handed a blank sheet of paper and asked to create and produce a pre-school series,' she recalls. 'There was no writer and the script was improvised.'

Indeed, the original pilot, with John Kane as presenter and Tim Wylton as a bear called 'Rainbow' (a character created by Lonsdale's husband, Reginald Collin) was not widely considered to be a winner. Although many of the elements were in place, such as three puppets named Zippy (created by researcher Sam Hanson), Sunshine and Moony and a musical group called Telltale, major changes were clearly called for.

A whole team of new talent was duly sought out, including writer John Kershaw (who had previously written for *Play School*), education adviser Jill Kent and fledgling designers Brian Cosgrove and Mark Hall who provided the dayglo titles and

links. As far as characters were concerned, Rainbow became Bungle, Sunshine and Moony disappeared while presenter Kane left for a career in serious theatre to be replaced by David Cook.

The first series went to air on 16 October 1972 and, although warmly received, undoubtedly benefited from a more generous time when programmes were not immediately judged according to their ratings. Nevertheless, Lonsdale was still not satisfied and planned a further series of bold changes to crack the formula they had been searching for all along.

'Rainbow aimed to entertain and educate, to stimulate children's imagination and to widen their experience,' she continues. 'We aimed to introduce them to new words,

new songs and new ideas. Each programme was to be based on a different theme, to which each item is related. And above all, *Rainbow* was to be fun.'

For Series Three, a new presenter was found in Geoffrey Hayes, an unlikely choice given his previous acting roles on police dramas such as *Dixon of Dock Green* and *Softly, Softly*. In recalling his audition, he concedes it was pure chance he even showed up.

'I was down at Thames on a few weeks off from *Z-Cars*. In fact, I was doing a part on a soap opera, when I bumped into two friends who were working on the programme. They told me the old presenter was leaving, so I raced up to the producer's [Lonsdale's] office and auditioned. A few weeks later it was whittled down to three and I got the job.'

Geoffrey was an immediate success, looking comfortable in a role few serious actors could have coped with. Even so, he had no idea it would hijack much of his future career.

'I thought it would be a fill-in, leaving me to get on with my other roles, but slowly it began to take over. It was better money – simple as that. But it was also an interesting gig and great fun; you got to act and dress up as well, I got to do voice-overs for the animations – it had everything you'd want to do as an actor.'

Arguably even more important was the addition of Roy Skelton. Already a prolific writer with previous credits for *Watch with Mother*, he went on in subsequent series to take over much of the writing duties, eventually penning over 100 of the show's 1,100-plus episodes.

'I was working on *Dr Who* at the time I was approached by Pam,' he recalls, 'and Peter Hawkins (a great voice man) had done Zippy in the first series. He did not want to do it any more and they auditioned nearly a hundred people to try out for the voice but with no success. Peter suggested me. Pam thought it was a no-no as she only knew me as a singer in musicals. However, I went to see her and it clicked. Originally I had to do a rough copy of Peter's voice, but in a little time I altered it considerably and made it my own … much coarser!'

Indeed, it was the new Zippy and George (introduced as 'very shy but loves singing and making strange noises') who emerged as the most memorable characters on the show. Always arguing and unlikely to last more than ten minutes together in the Big

Brother house, they managed to be bigger than the sum of their differences and a worthy rival to that other famous odd couple, *Sesame Street*'s Ernie and Bert. The fact that Zippy still gets to star in commercials and comedy shows thirty years later, without the benefit of re-runs or major merchandising, speaks volumes for Skelton's wit and flexibility as a writer and performer. He too, however, had no idea it would last so long.

'I thought it was at the most a six-week job! There were times when I was offered exciting stage and film productions which I couldn't do because they clashed with *Rainbow*, or it would mean signing for a West End production that would mean I could possibly be booked for a year and so would have to give up *Rainbow*. Yes, there have been times when I have wondered if it was progressive to stay on … but … I loved doing it. There were always new and exciting things to try out.'

Series Three, which aired on 29 October 1973, also saw the addition of regular puppeteer Ronnie le Drew and Stanley Bates as Bungle, while the music was provided by a new group of Julian Littman, Charmian Dore and Karl Johnson (opposite). In another bold step, previously only attempted by *Jackanory*, heavyweight actors such as Judy Dench, Beryl Reid and Julian Glover were drafted in to narrate the short stories.

However, even though the show had now begun to catch on, Lonsdale had not yet finished with the changes. The final elements were in place in time for Series Four, with Rod Burton, Jane Tucker and Matthew Corbett (below) providing the music – composing and interweaving their own songs in a way many children's programmes

tried, but very few successfully achieved. Corbett eventually left, to concentrate on the family dynasty that was *Sooty*, to be replaced first by Roger Walker (below, on the right) and finally in 1980 by Freddy Marks.

Now, with the regular cast in place, the series moved seamlessly on, never off the air for more than a few weeks and lapped up by countries as far-flung as Australia, Zimbabwe and Jordan. Meanwhile, the characters of Zippy and George were already permeating popular culture, becoming the mainstay of 1980s impersonators like Bobby Davro (see page 119) and Jim Davidson. The appeal of the programme, however, owed just as much to a cast that was clearly at ease working together.

Left to right: Ronnie Le Drew, Roy Skelton and Malcolm Lord

'We all got on wonderfully well,' recalls Roy (below), 'and I am happy to say, even with all the ups and downs of a twenty-year period, we are all still friends. I think of the fun of Rod, Jane and Freddy doing the final camera rehearsal of a musical number set inside a garden set, with three of us getting behind a hedge and holding up signs which said "Nudist Colony" and walking behind it so that all the cameras could see was the top half of our naked bodies. The fun was that Rod, Jane and Freddy were unaware and carried on performing immaculately to camera.'

Director Dennis Kirkland recalls that some of the camaraderie was born out of pure necessity. 'We never used to have any money, all we had was ideas. The brilliance of the cast and crew was to invent things without a penny – we used to steal scenery from other shows in the hope that Max Bygraves wouldn't be needing it in five minutes. Of course, you can mime a door, but if you could steal it, steal it.'

He also recalls how *Rainbow*'s influence spread far beyond Thames and, as with all things innocent, occasionally lent itself to distinctly adult parody. 'When Thames was at its height, we [Eric and Ernie, Les Dawson, Jim Davidson] all used to work together in the same studios and everybody adored *Rainbow*. We were all buddies. Later, when we did the Freddie Starr show, we always had the *Rainbow* lads on and in the dress rehearsals we hammed it up for the lads – believe me, it was beyond filth. I'm sure the tapes are somewhere.'

During its twenty-year run, the show was notable for collecting a rich variety of talents who went down very different paths. Original writer John Kershaw was carving out a promising career as a Hollywood scriptwriter until his untimely death at the age of fifty, while John

Leeson (the original Bungle) went back to straight acting and the voice of Dr Who's K9. Hugh Fraser was part of Telltale, Rainbow's original musical group, and ironically was sacked by Lonsdale for his inability to act. Now an accomplished screen actor, he is best known as Captain Hastings, sidekick to David Suchet's Inspector Poirot. Meanwhile, Kirkland married one of the show's researchers, Mary Austin, before going on to many light entertainment shows such as *Name That Tune* and *Sykes* but most memorably a twenty-year association with Benny Hill as director and producer.

Another element frequently overlooked is the skill and versatility of the puppeteers, with a whole host of people pulling the strings at one time or another. Stanley Bates stuck it out the longest in that stifling Bungle costume (he and Geoffrey also wrote many of the scripts) before leaving the show to run a string of antiques shops. He was replaced as Bungle by the equally proficient Malcolm Lord, who had previously worked on George. Ronnie le Drew undoubtedly stayed the longest, operating both Zippy and George in his time, moving up to voicing Zippy in *Rainbow*'s final and most controversial chapter.

Of course, by the 1980s children's TV was never just about programme making. Although still in its infancy, *Masters of the Universe* and *Transformers* had proven the power of merchandising and the producers of *Rainbow* were never blind to a good commercial spin-off. There were albums and annuals and the usual array of lunch-boxes and activity kits, but more ambitious ideas too. Big-money live tours may now be commonplace for the likes of Bob the Builder and the Tweenies, but it was *Rainbow* that started the trend, providing a lucrative sideline for the cast whenever they were not filming.

'We went off to do panto,' recalls Geoffrey, 'and the Rainbow Roadshow started in the late 80s, allowing us to tour the country doing a proper stage show which used to pack 'em out. On a Saturday at somewhere like the Liverpool Empire, which holds over 2,000 people, we used to do three shows, all sold out.'

Nor was the show without its controversy, including a few suitably juicy half-myths which the tabloids seized upon with relish. One late 1980s headline proclaimed: 'Love swap secrets of TV stars', alleging a bizarre love-triangle between Rod, Jane and Freddy (right). Of course, the truth was much less lurid – Jane and Rod had indeed been married but were in the process of divorcing long before Freddy joined the cast. And although

Jane and Freddy have now lived together for nearly twenty years, the group remains close friends.

'If Freddy had anything to do with the break-up,' explains Jane, 'do you honestly think we would still be working together?'

Then there was the infamous 'Rude Rainbow' incident, an apparently full episode of the show written in 1979 for an annual (but strictly private) competition between the major ITV companies. Allegedly penned by Roy in a single afternoon and directed by Kirkland, it features George counting while peeling a banana ('One skin, Two skin, Three skin …' etc.) and the song 'Pluck, pluck, pluck away!' 'Rude Rainbow' duly won

the cup that year, and although videotapes of the programme are known to exist, no one outside the inner circle of edit suites and senior TV executives admits to owning a copy.

Most controversial of all, though, was the unhappy way the series finally ended. By the end of 1992 Thames TV had lost its franchise. A new production company, Tetra Films, had picked up the show and set about making more radical changes. The new *Rainbow* emerged in 1994, featuring only some of the original crew. It centred around a toy shop owned by Mr Top and staffed by Zippy, George and Bungle plus a new puppet, Cleo the Rabbit (above). Zippy was voiced by *Rainbow* stalwart Ronnie le Drew, with new actors taking George, Bungle and Cleo.

Admittedly, with the rapid demise of other long-running shows like *Watch with Mother* and *Play School* it was clear that *Rainbow* did need to evolve. However, the way the producers handled these changes appears to have been tactless at best. Sadly, Geoffrey claims to have heard the news of his sacking from the tabloids rather than Tetra.

'I was shocked really, and for a couple of days I thought it was just me who had been dropped. But then RJ&F had already left and of course Roy had now been dropped too, the guy playing Bungle – he was history, as was the puppeteer doing George – only the Zippy puppeteer was left. I don't think the controllers realized quite what they were doing; Bungle looked different and even though Zippy and George looked much the same, it wasn't Roy and so it wasn't them. They battled on for a bit, but it just faded away.'

Rainbow was to resurface one last time in 1996 as *Rainbow Days*, a slight re-working of Tetra's previous rework with a new presenter (Dale Superville, below) and a more sketch-based format. Few people, however, would rate it among their favourites.

'It is fair to say that was I saddened,' says Roy, with admirable restraint. 'I didn't think it came up the standard we had all always strived to achieve.'

Despite a brief *Rainbow Days* comic produced by Spiderman and X-Men veterans Marvel, it was all over by the end of 1997. In one form or another, *Rainbow* had lasted twenty-five years, making it ITV's longest-running kids' show by far.

Since the show ended, there have been highs and lows for the cast, often proving that the fabled *Blue Peter* curse does not apply merely to one programme. While the title designers went on to found Cosgrove Hall, stable of such classics as *Danger Mouse* and *Count Duckula*, Rod, Jane and Freddy never sought TV exposure again, preferring to take a different route via albums and tours.

'After *Rainbow*,' says Jane, 'we moved straight to touring with Rod, Jane and Freddy's show, which we did for six years and that got us nicely over it. It was sad when we had to finish, but instead of waiting for another TV show we just went straight on the road. We bridged the gap.'

Geoffrey, however, confesses to finding the change a little harder at first. 'I was waiting for the phone to ring … I couldn't get any acting work, because I was just thought of as a presenter – so it was down to pantos and summer seasons, a few children's stories. I became a jobbing actor again.'

In 2000 he did emerge in a commercial for Virginmoney.com, driving a taxi as he has done

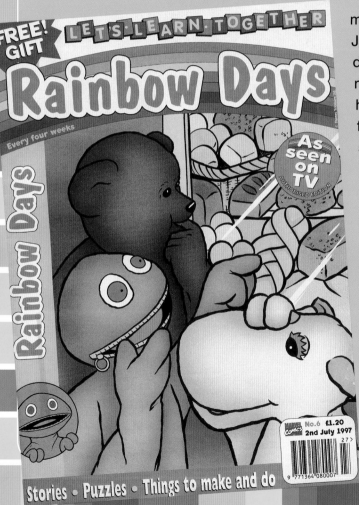

FREE! GIFT

LET'S·LEARN·TOGETHER

Rainbow Days

Every four weeks

Rainbow Days

As seen on TV
AUTHORISED EDITION

MARVEL COMICS No.6 £1.20 2nd July 1997

27 >

9 771364 080007

Stories · Puzzles · Things to make and do

occasionally ever since. More recently, he seems to have rediscovered his old vigour, making numerous personal appearances and, in 2002, taking a one-man show entitled 'Over the Rainbow' to the Edinburgh Festival. So, all in all, no regrets? 'It was twenty fantastic years and I'd do it again. Even ten years on, I still get letters and stopped in the street – it's amazing.'

Roy also maintains there was certainly gold to be found at the end of the Rainbow. 'It bought me a house, helped my wife and I bring up two super children and we had and still have some great holidays. I look back on *Rainbow* with fondness – and not just fondness, but lots of happiness and joy.'

After the end of the show, Roy continued writing and performing, fitted in a decade of pantomime work and still found his plans for well-earned retirement thwarted by the enduring popularity of Zippy and George. These

days he can be found talking loudly on the subject in interviews, conventions and even the odd Marmite commercial. 'And one day soon, I am going to write either the great novel or my much more boring life story,' he adds.

Finally, of course, there was the woman who started the whole multi-coloured journey and took the wheel for the first five years. Pamela Lonsdale (above) went on to co-devise and produce the popular 1970s drama series *Ace of Wands*, a stage musical, and several other shows before become executive producer of children's drama for Thames TV. Since 1984 she has been a prolific freelance producer and director, and although now semi-retired, still finds one show leaping to the front of most people's memories.

'Working on *Rainbow* was exciting and stimulating,' she says. 'The teamwork was terrific. Everyone – casts, the writer, researchers, directors, production assistants, and the

studio crews – worked tremendously hard, and it is largely due to them that it was such a great success, and is remembered today by so many viewers. I am very proud of it.'

So what next for *Rainbow*? Well, apart from this book, produced in irreverent but affectionate praise to *Rainbow*'s thirtieth anniversary in October 2002, many of the cast still keep the torch moving. The 'Rod, Jane and Freddy Show' has toured regularly since the 1980s and in 2001 'The Rainbow Disco Roadshow' took to the stage with George and Zippy notching up over seventy dates in six months, deejaying at universities and clubs and occasionally joined by Geoffrey and Bungle. There is even talk of a summer dance-remix of the theme song, penned by Tim Thomas, Hugh Fraser and Hugh Portnow and still instantly recognizable to millions.

Meanwhile the unofficial website http://www.rainbow.web.com, lovingly maintained by two enthusiasts, has received over 250,000 hits despite minimal promotion and we can safely assume the characters will keep popping up in shows like BBC1's *Dead*

Ringers (on which Zippy was portrayed as Cherie Blair). One thing is certain: we haven't seen the last of them.

Sadly, however, despite the tremendous success of other kids' classics like *Bill and Ben* and *Thunderbirds*, there are no immediate plans to either repeat or recommission the show for TV. This seems to fly in the face of its continuing popularity (it recently came in at number 7 in Channel 4's 'Top 100 Kids' TV Shows') and ignores the fact that many of the cast would still jump at the chance. So could it still happen?

'Who knows?' concludes Roy. 'I would love to do some more and perhaps …? Well, we shall see.'

And so, after ten years off-air, we must wait and see. Undoubtedly *Rainbow* will be revisited one day, as all successful TV formats are – but whether it would recapture the original charm without the classic cast is highly debatable. To most of us the classic *Rainbow* line-up will always be Geoffrey, Roy, Stan/ Malcolm, Rod, Jane and Freddy – timeless fun made by big kids for little ones. You may not recognize all the names, but the colours have lasted longer than anyone could have imagined.

NB: Special thanks to the following for their help in this chapter: Pamela Lonsdale, Geoffrey Hayes, Roy Skelton, Jane Tucker, Russell Michaels, Mary and Dennis Kirkland, Andrew and Caroline Barrett